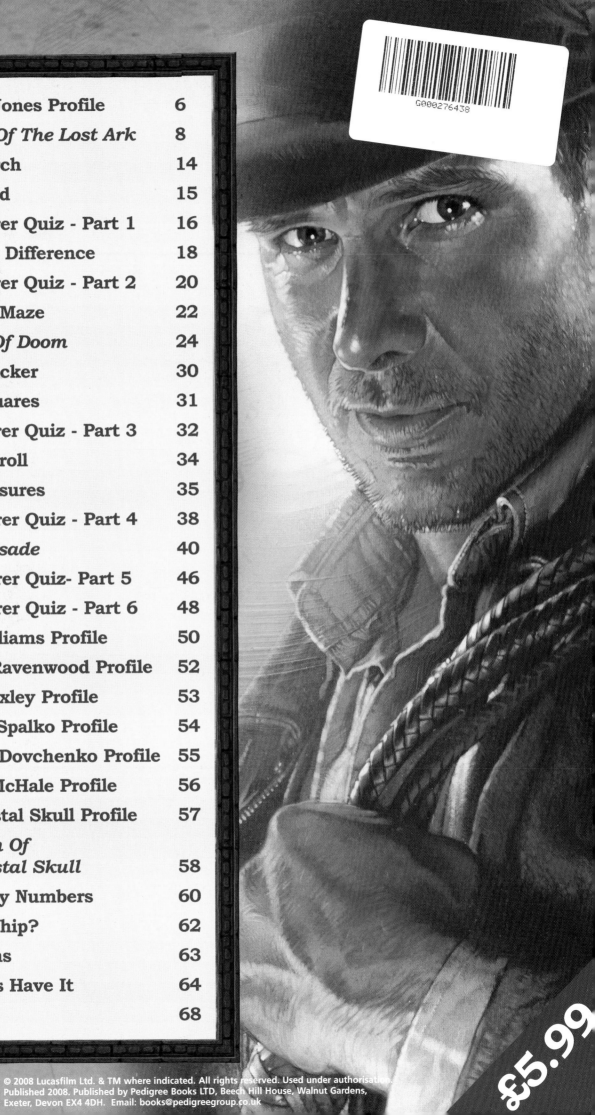

£5.99

Pedigree

© 2008 Lucasfilm Ltd. & TM where indicated. All rights reserved. Used under authorisation.
Published 2008. Published by Pedigree Books LTD, Beech Hill House, Walnut Gardens,
Exeter, Devon EX4 4DH. Email: books@pedigreegroup.co.uk

G000276438

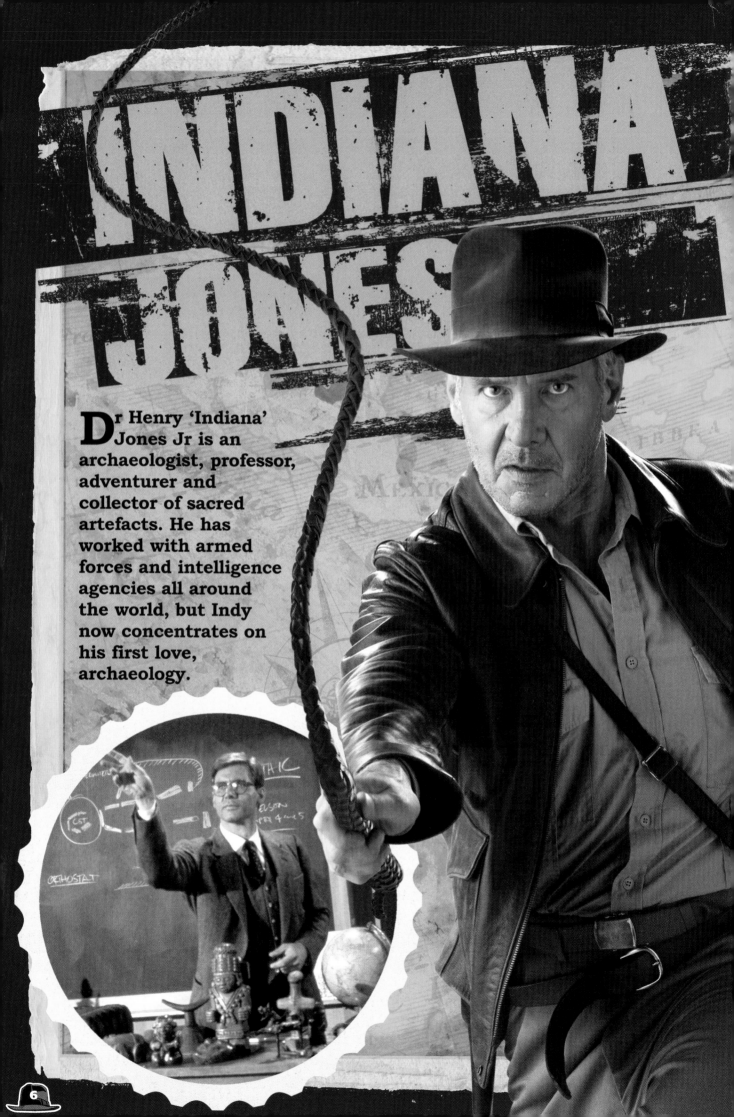

INDIANA JONES

Dr Henry 'Indiana' Jones Jr is an archaeologist, professor, adventurer and collector of sacred artefacts. He has worked with armed forces and intelligence agencies all around the world, but Indy now concentrates on his first love, archaeology.

During his holidays from the university, Dr Jones, otherwise known as Indy, often goes on missions to far-flung corners of the planet. He seeks out rare artefacts, most of which are purchased by the National Museum. On his many adventures, Indy has discovered several objects that were thought to be myths or lost long ago. His searches often put him at odds with the authorities, his fellow archaeologists and the enemies of the United States.

All his life, Indy has tried to live up to the reputation of his father, Henry Jones Sr, who is also an archaeologist. The two men are very different, but they share a lot of the same character traits – more than Indy would ever admit to!

RAIDERS of the LOST ARK

It is 1936 and Dr Indiana Jones is in Peru trying to discover an ancient idol. However, after risking his life to recover the treasure, it is stolen by his long-time enemy, Belloq! Furious and frustrated, Indy has to return home empty-handed.

Army Intelligence gives Indy a mission. He must find the Ark of the Covenant, the resting place of the Ten Commandments. Legend says that its power can wipe out entire armies. However, Hitler has also sent his soldiers after the long-lost Ark. Indy must find it before the Nazis!

Indy goes to Patan, Nepal. He visits a bar that is run by his ex-girlfriend, Marion Ravenwood, who is not happy to see him. Indy explains that he is looking for a medallion that Marion's father, Dr Abner Ravenwood, found on one of his archaeological digs. Marion claims that she doesn't have the medallion and Indy leaves. But as soon as he has gone, Nazi soldiers arrive at Marion's bar. They are looking for exactly the same thing!

Marion is scared. She told Indy a lie – she *does* have the medallion. The Nazis are about to torture her when Indy returns and leaps into action. His fighting skills take the Nazis completely by surprise! Soon the bar is a seething mass of fighting men. Suddenly flames leap up – the bar is on fire!

Toht, a Nazi interrogator, spots the medallion lying on the floor and lunges for it. He doesn't realise that the medallion has become red hot in the fire! The boiling-hot coin burns an imprint of itself on to his palm and Toht screams in agony.

Indy grabs both the medallion and Marion, and escapes in the nick of time.

In Cairo in Egypt, Indy and Marion find Indy's old friend, Sallah, who is reluctantly working for the Nazis on a mysterious digging operation. Indy knows what they are looking for!

There is no time to relax – the Nazis know that Indy is there! After a high-speed chase through the streets of Cairo, Marion is captured and stuffed into a basket on the back of a truck carrying explosives to the site of the Nazi dig. Indy fires his revolver at the driver and the truck crashes and explodes!

Indy is horrified by what he has done – Marion was on that truck! But there is little time to grieve. Indy's old enemy Belloq is leading the dig for the Nazis and they believe that they are close to finding the Ark.

The Nazis, under the command of an officer called Dietrich, are using the image that was burned on to Toht's hand, but they are digging over a mile away from their target.

Indy creeps into the Nazi camp and uses the medallion to find the exact spot where the Well of Souls, the rumoured resting place of the Ark, is positioned. He also finds Marion – she is still alive but a prisoner! Marion is delighted to see Indy, but she can't believe it when he refuses to free her. Indy cannot risk letting the Nazis know that he is there.

Indy leads a secret team of diggers to the real location of the Well of Souls. They dig all night and at last they hit stone. Excitedly, they pull back a huge stone tablet and find an entrance.

As Sallah peers down into the vault, he notices that the floor is moving! Indy drops a torch down and then freezes in terror. The crypt below is covered with the one thing he fears: snakes!

Indy won't allow his fear to stop him reaching the Ark! Sallah and his team lower Indy into the well. He sprays gasoline over the hundreds of snakes and sets them on fire – that should keep them at bay for a while!

Sallah and Indy load the sacred Ark into a crate and order their men to pull it up to the surface. Sallah goes up next, but the rope is not sent back down. Boiling with anger, Indy recognises the familiar laugh of Belloq. Once again his enemy has stolen a priceless treasure from him.

Marion is thrown down into the pit and the entrance is sealed. When the torches go out, the snakes will attack. Indy and Marion have to find a way out!

Indy spots some snakes coming in through a wall on the far side of the crypt. He topples a huge statue over and knocks a massive hole in the wall. Marion and Indy escape as the last of the torches goes out.

Indy risks his life and manages to get the Ark back! Sallah introduces Marion and Indy to a man called Katanga, the captain of a tramp steamer. They put the Ark in the hold and set off.

It seems as if Indy has beaten Belloq and the Nazis once and for all!

Suddenly, the crew of a German U-boat boards the ship. Katanga has betrayed them to the enemy! The Nazis take the Ark and Marion. However, Indy manages to sneak on board the U-boat unseen.

The Nazi U-boat travels to an island in the Mediterranean ocean. Belloq has planned a secret ritual that will reveal the contents of the Ark. The Nazis carry the Ark to a temple high in the island's mountains. An altar has been set up ready for the ceremony. Indy has to act!

Carrying a rocket launcher, Indy threatens to destroy the Ark, but Nazi guards sneak up behind him. Indy is taken prisoner! The Ark is carried into the temple and placed at the altar.

As Belloq recites the ancient text, two soldiers remove the lid of the Ark. It is full of dust! Suddenly, ghostly apparitions begin to emerge from it. Then a shaft of blinding light rises from the Ark. Jets of flame shoot into the crowd of soldiers, killing them all instantly. Indy screams at Marion to shut her eyes. They must not look, or they will be destroyed!

The heat of the flames intensifies and the Nazi officers melt into a pool of goo. Belloq's body is engulfed by flame until it explodes. A shaft of fire rockets high into the air and then drops back down into the Ark, which seals itself shut.

Back in the United States, Indy hands over the Ark to a pair of government officials. Thanks to him, it is safe from the clutches of the evil Nazis!

WORD SEARCH

Use all your archaeological skills to find the lost words in this grid. Look closely as they are very well hidden!

```
C B R U A W Z K V W A L E C S
J R O E E M R N H D A A N X J
W W Y V V A A I P R D S A J M
G N F S T L P Z C C C T L D C
L K M S T R O H O H L C P Y S
D G O V K A A V G N M R O L X
B L R M D E L J E S R U R A M
K S Q X O S H S U R W S E F C
P U Y L R J H O K V E A A E S
J I O W V P T M L U H D W D Q
Y G E L I P H E J I L E Y O V
Y P A R T Y B O O B T L H R V
G O S J S D R H H Q U B W A S
J D J T E M P L E O F D O O M
Z P J J U N G L E U X I S X B
```

AEROPLANE
AMAZON
ARCHAEOLOGY
BOOBY TRAP
CRYSTAL SKULL
FEDORA

JUNGLE
LAST CRUSADE
LOST ARK
REVOLVER
TEMPLE OF DOOM
WHIP

14

CROSS WORD

Solve the clues and complete the puzzle.

Across

4. The best digger in Egypt and an old friend of Indy's. (6)
6. A Nazi interrogator who burned his hand on Marion's medallion. (4)
8. Indy's biggest fear. (6)

Down

1. The resting place of the Lost Ark. (3,4,2,5)
2. Indy's enemy in Raiders Of The Lost Ark. (6)
3. Indy's ex-girlfriend. (6)
5. The boat captain who betrayed Indy and Marion. (7)
7. The leader of the Nazis searching for the Ark. (8)

ADVENTURER QUIZ

Part I

Do you have what it takes to become an intrepid adventurer just like Indiana Jones? Take these quizzes to see if you can survive all the obstacles! Add up your scores from each quiz to see if you are qualified to join Indy on his next adventure.

1

In what year does Indiana Jones go in search of the Lost Ark?

A :: 1935 ☐
B :: 1936 ☐
C :: 1937 ☐

2

Who is this fellow archaeologist and one of Indy's greatest rivals?

A :: ABNER RAVENWOOD ☐
B :: DIETRICH ☐
C :: BELLOQ ☐

3

What is the Lost Ark thought to contain?

A :: THE TEN COMMANDMENTS ☐
B :: THE HOLY GRAIL ☐
C :: EXCALIBUR ☐

4

Who says:
*"Dr Jones...
again we see
there is nothing
you can possess
which I cannot
take away."?*

A :: SALLAH ☐
B :: DIETRICH ☐
C :: BELLOQ ☐

5

Who is this?

A :: MARION
RAVENWOOD ☐
B :: TOHT ☐
C :: SALLAH ☐

6

Who says:
*"Listen, Herr
Mack, I don't
know what kind
of people you're
used to dealing
with, but nobody
tells me what to
do in my place!"?*

A :: TOHT ☐
B :: MARION ☐
C :: INDY ☐

7

What is the
name of the
resting place of
the Ark?

A :: TANIS ☐
B :: THE WELL
OF LOST SOULS ☐
C :: EL DORADO ☐

8

"_____. I hate
_____." What is
the missing word
from this quote?

A :: SNAKES ☐
B :: NAZIS ☐
C :: BELLOQ ☐

Answers
Give yourself one point
for every correct answer.
Make a note of your scores
from this round and move on
to the next challenge.
1b, 2c, 3a, 4c, 5a, 6b, 7b, 8a

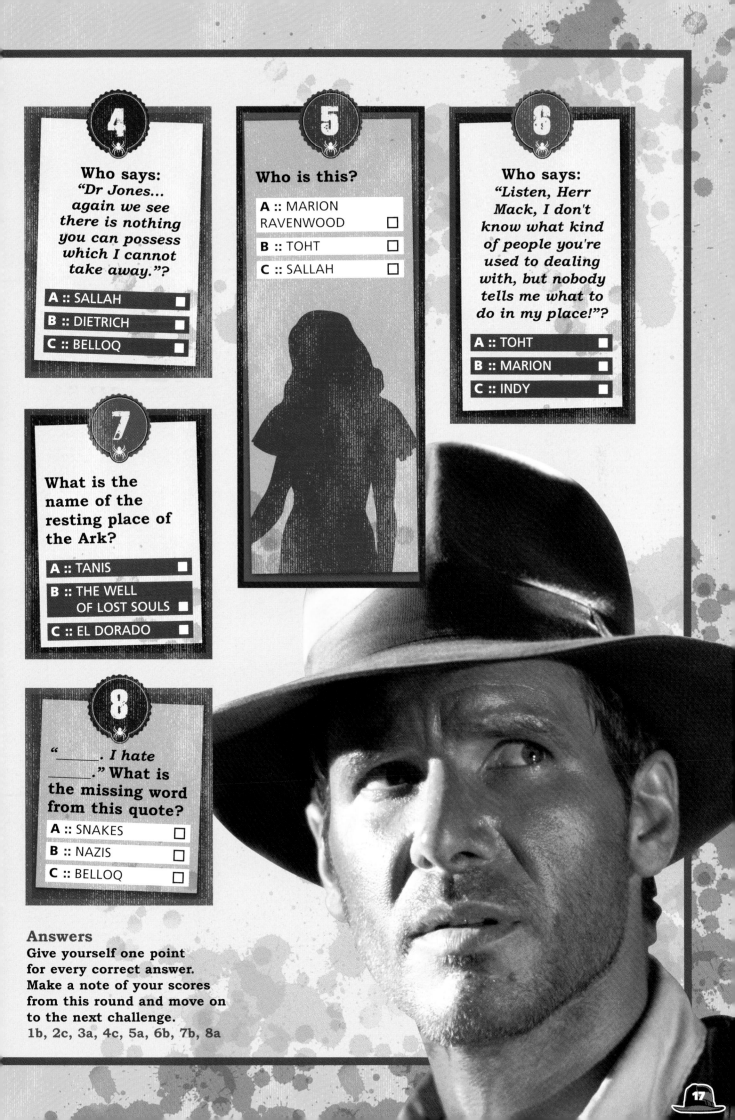

SPOT THE DIFFERENCE

Look at these two pictures from Raiders of the Lost Ark. Can you spot the ten differences? You will need to be eagle-eyed, just like Indy!

The **10** differences are...

1. _____
2. _____
3. _____
4. _____
5. _____
6. _____
7. _____
8. _____
9. _____
10. _____

ADVENTURER QUIZ Part 2

Congratulations! You got past the first round of questions, but it only gets harder from now on. Do you know your stuff?

9

What is the name of the captain who offers Indy and Marion a place on his ship?

A :: KATANGA ☐
B :: SATIPO ☐
C :: BRODY ☐

10

In which country is Marion's bar?

A :: NEPAL ☐
B :: CHINA ☐
C :: MEXICO ☐

11

What is the name of the boat that attempts to carry Indy, Marion and the Ark to England?

A :: BANTU WIND ☐
B :: BANTU SPEED ☐
C :: BANTU STEAM ☐

12

Who is this?

A :: KATANGA ☐
B :: DIETRICH ☐
C :: TOHT ☐

13

The medallion that both Indy and the Nazis want from Marion is the headpiece to which of the following?

A :: STAFF OF JA ☐
B :: STAFF OF KA ☐
C :: STAFF OF RA ☐

14

Who stops Indy from eating a poisoned date in Cairo?

A :: MARION ☐
B :: MARCUS BRODY ☐
C :: SALLAH ☐

15

Who is this good friend of Indy's?

A :: MARCUS BRODY ☐
B :: SALLAH ☐
C :: KATANGA ☐

16

Who says: "Jones is dead. I killed him. He was of no use to us."?

A :: BELLOQ ☐
B :: TOHT ☐
C :: KATANGA ☐

Answers
Give yourself one point for every correct answer. Make a note of your scores from this round and move on to the next challenge.
9a, 10a, 11a, 12b, 13c, 14c, 15a, 16c

MYSTICAL MAZE

START

FINISH

Work your way through the first maze, taking care to avoid all the booby traps, snakes and bad guys! When you have found your way out of the ancient city, travel on to the Amazon jungle and find a safe route to the kingdom of the crystal skull!

START

FINISH

INDIANA JONES

and the
TEMPLE OF DOOM ™

It is 1935 and in Shanghai, Dr Indiana Jones walks into a nightclub called Obi-Wan. The singer Willie Scott is performing on stage. Indy is there to meet three Chinese men. They hired him to find an artefact that holds the remains of a Chinese Emperor.

The men give Indy a huge diamond in return for the artefact. They offer him a drink to celebrate the deal, but as he drinks, they laugh. They have poisoned him! They offer Indy the antidote – in exchange for the diamond.

Indy picks up a flaming kebab and hurls it at one of the men. When his revolver goes off, there is pandemonium in the nightclub! People race for the doors as Indy lunges for the antidote. It skids across the floor and into the sea of people. Then Willie grabs the antidote and she and Indy leap out of the window!

They land in a car, driven by Indy's sidekick, Short Round. Indy, Short Round and Willie speed to a nearby airport, where they board a plane. They seem to have escaped the Chinese boss, Lao Che. Unfortunately, Lao Che owns the plane they have just boarded!

While their passengers sleep, the pilots dump the remaining fuel and parachute out of the plane. Luckily, Willie wakes up and realises what has happened. Indy grabs a self-inflating emergency raft and tells Willie and Shorty to hold on. It's their only chance!

Indy, Willie and Shorty leap from the plane, clinging to the raft, which inflates like a parachute. They land on the snowy mountain below, and the raft becomes a sled and hurtles down the mountainside at death-defying speed.

Indy and his companions survive and soon find themselves in a cursed Indian village. The villagers believe that evil spirits have taken their children away because their sacred Sankara stone was stolen. They beg Indy to find their lost children. Indy agrees to help and he, Short Round and Willie set off on elephants to Pankot Palace.

When they arrive at the palace, Indy, Shorty and Willie are invited to dinner with the Maharajah. The meal doesn't impress Willie. The main course of snake surprise (a giant python filled with live baby snakes) is bad enough, but the dessert of chilled monkey brains is just too much!

That night, a soldier attacks Indy in his room. Indy soon deals with him, but it's clear that they are in danger. Indy and Shorty dash into Willie's room to check that she is safe.

When Indy searches Willie's room for assassins, he discovers a hidden passage! Indy and Shorty step into the tunnel, and soon find themselves in a large chamber. Human skeletons are scattered over the floor. Indy guesses that the room is a trap, but Shorty triggers it! The roof of the room starts to lower and spikes rise up through the floor.

Indy and Shorty scream for Willie to help them. She enters the tunnel, plunges her hand into a gap in the wall and pulls a lever. The trap is disarmed, but the adventure isn't over yet. Willie accidentally sets the trap off again! They escape from the chamber just in time.

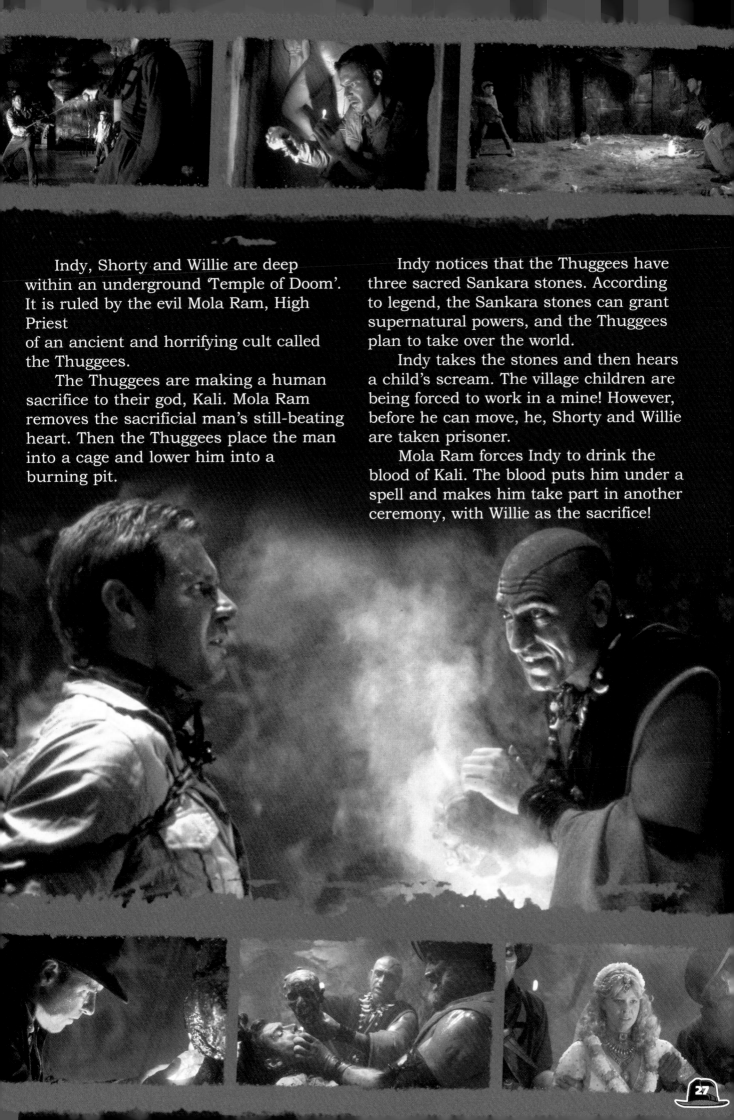

Indy, Shorty and Willie are deep within an underground 'Temple of Doom'. It is ruled by the evil Mola Ram, High Priest of an ancient and horrifying cult called the Thuggees.

The Thuggees are making a human sacrifice to their god, Kali. Mola Ram removes the sacrificial man's still-beating heart. Then the Thuggees place the man into a cage and lower him into a burning pit.

Indy notices that the Thuggees have three sacred Sankara stones. According to legend, the Sankara stones can grant supernatural powers, and the Thuggees plan to take over the world.

Indy takes the stones and then hears a child's scream. The village children are being forced to work in a mine! However, before he can move, he, Shorty and Willie are taken prisoner.

Mola Ram forces Indy to drink the blood of Kali. The blood puts him under a spell and makes him take part in another ceremony, with Willie as the sacrifice!

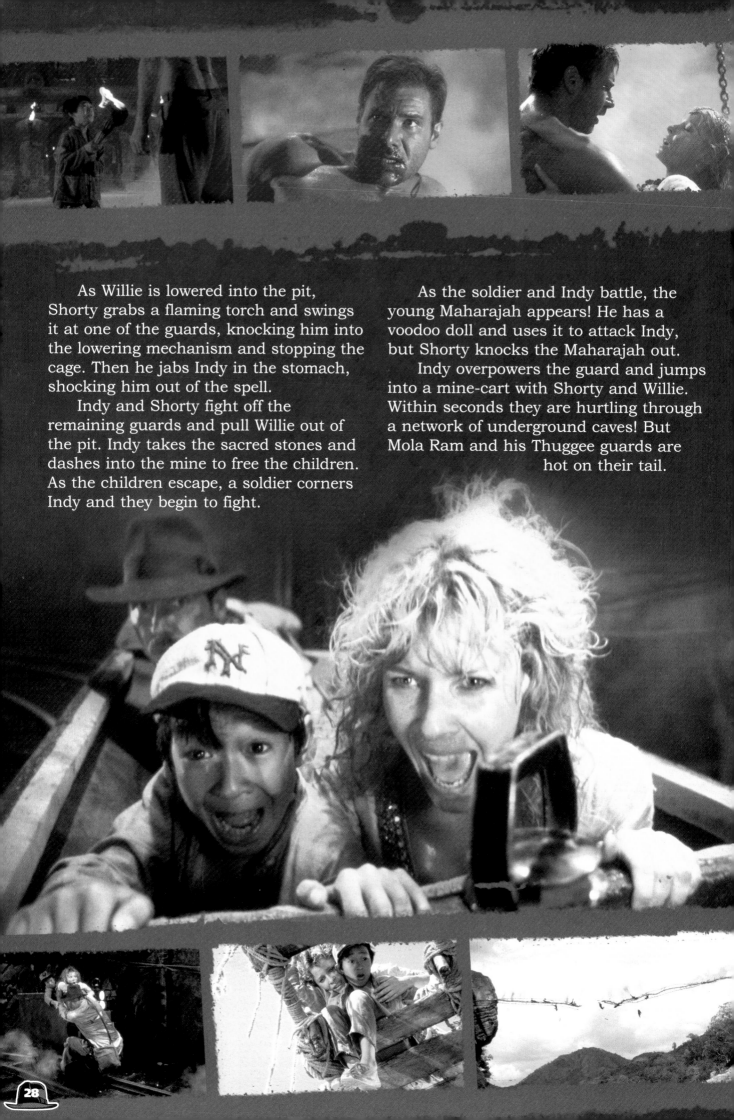

As Willie is lowered into the pit, Shorty grabs a flaming torch and swings it at one of the guards, knocking him into the lowering mechanism and stopping the cage. Then he jabs Indy in the stomach, shocking him out of the spell.

Indy and Shorty fight off the remaining guards and pull Willie out of the pit. Indy takes the sacred stones and dashes into the mine to free the children. As the children escape, a soldier corners Indy and they begin to fight.

As the soldier and Indy battle, the young Maharajah appears! He has a voodoo doll and uses it to attack Indy, but Shorty knocks the Maharajah out.

Indy overpowers the guard and jumps into a mine-cart with Shorty and Willie. Within seconds they are hurtling through a network of underground caves! But Mola Ram and his Thuggee guards are hot on their tail.

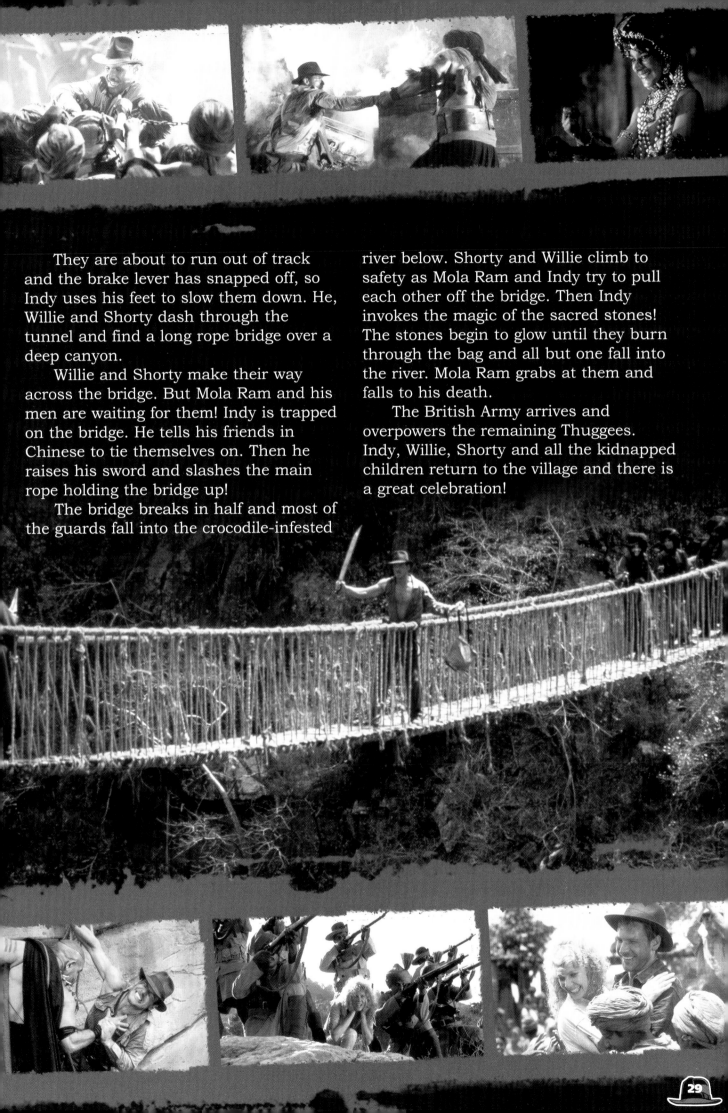

They are about to run out of track and the brake lever has snapped off, so Indy uses his feet to slow them down. He, Willie and Shorty dash through the tunnel and find a long rope bridge over a deep canyon.

Willie and Shorty make their way across the bridge. But Mola Ram and his men are waiting for them! Indy is trapped on the bridge. He tells his friends in Chinese to tie themselves on. Then he raises his sword and slashes the main rope holding the bridge up!

The bridge breaks in half and most of the guards fall into the crocodile-infested river below. Shorty and Willie climb to safety as Mola Ram and Indy try to pull each other off the bridge. Then Indy invokes the magic of the sacred stones! The stones begin to glow until they burn through the bag and all but one fall into the river. Mola Ram grabs at them and falls to his death.

The British Army arrives and overpowers the remaining Thuggees. Indy, Willie, Shorty and all the kidnapped children return to the village and there is a great celebration!

CODE CRACKER

The Nazis are hot on Indy's trail. Can you help him to crack this coded message? Indy has already made a start. He has worked out what some of the symbols mean.

1. Look carefully at the message and see if you can guess what any of the words might be.
2. Fill in the missing letters and discover which symbols represent which letters.
3. When you figure out which letter a symbol stands for, write it into the decoder.

A	B	C	D	E	F	G	H	I	J	K	L	M
O		ς	Λ			E		ϑ			Θ	Ξ

N	O	P	Q	R	S	T	U	V	W	X	Y	Z
I							Σ		Π			

ΦΤ   ΧΟΣΤ   ΑΔΟςΜΤΛ   ΛΩςΑΩΔ   ϑΩΙΤΝ
(A V) *(A C)* *(D)* *(D C)* *(J N)*

ΑΩ   ςΟΓΔΩ,   ΤΕΗΚΑ.   ΦΤ   ΥΤΘΓΤΣΤ   ΧΤ
(C A) *(G)* *(L)* *(V)*

ΦΓΘΘ   ΥΤ   ΞΤΤΑΓΙΕ   ΧΓΝ   ΩΘΛ   ψΔΓΤΙΛ
(L L) *(M)* *(N G)* *(L D)* *(N D)*

ΝΟΘΘΟΧ   ΓΙ   ΟΙ   ΟΑΑΤΞΚΑ   ΑΩ   ΛΓΝςΩΣΤΔ
(A L L A) *(N)* *(A N)* *(A)* *(M)* *(D)* *(C V)*

ΑΧΤ   ΘΩςΟΑΓΩΙ   ΩψΟΔΜ.   ΦΤ   ΦΓΘΘ
(L) *(C A)* *(N)* *(A)* *(L L)*

ΓΙΑΤΔςΤΚΑ   ΧΓΞ   ΟΝ   ΧΤ   ΥΩΟΔΛΝ   Ο
(N) *(C)* *(M)* *(A)* *(A D)* *(A)*

ΚΟΛΛΘΤ   ΝΑΤΟΞΤΔ   ΩΙ   ΑΧΤ   ΔΓΣΤΔ   ΙΓΘΤ.
(A D D) *(A M)* *(N)* *(V)* *(N)*

ΦΤ   ςΟΙ   ΙΩΑ   ΘΤΑ   ΧΓΞ   ΔΤΟςΧ   ΧΓΝ
(C A N N) *(M)* *(A C)*

ΛΤΝΑΓΙΟΑΓΩΙ.   ΑΧΓΝ   ΓΝ   Ο   ΛΓΔΤςΑ   ΩΔΛΤΔ
(D) *(N A)* *(N)* *(A)* *(D)* *(C)* *(D)*

ψΔΩΞ   ΛΓΤΑΔΓςΧ.
(M) *(D)* *(C)*

SKULL SQUARES

Follow the arrow clues Indy has set out for you and travel through the skull grid. Mark your path with a thick pen. If you travel through a square that contains an ancient treasure, tick it off in the box below. How many treasures will you collect?

TICK OFF THE TREASURES YOU COLLECTED

ADVENTURER QUIZ Part 3

You have escaped from the Well of Souls! Well done, but don't get overconfident. Now you have to navigate your way through the dreaded Temple of Doom!

17

What is the name of the nightclub where Indy first meets Willie Scot?

A :: CLUB JEDI ☐

B :: CLUB OBI-WAN ☐

C :: CLUB DEATH STAR ☐

18

With what does Lao Che pay Indy for finding the artefact?

A :: A DIAMOND ☐

B :: CASH ☐

C :: A TREASURE MAP ☐

19

Who is this?

A :: LAO CHE ☐

B :: SHORT ROUND ☐

C :: MOLA RAM ☐

20

Who says:
"I always thought that archaeologists were always funny looking men going around looking for their mummies."?

A :: CHATTAR LAL ☐
B :: WILLIE SCOTT ☐
C :: MARCUS BRODY ☐

21

How many lines are engraved on the sacred Shankara stone?

A :: 1 ☐
B :: 2 ☐
C :: 3 ☐

22

What is the name of the cult of which Mola Ram is a leader?

A :: HUGGEE ☐
B :: BUGGEE ☐
C :: THUGGEE ☐

23

In which mountain range does Indy, Willie and Shorty's plane crash?

A :: THE ANDES ☐
B :: THE ALPS ☐
C :: THE HIMALAYAS ☐

24

Who is this?

A :: MOLA RAM ☐
B :: LAO CHE ☐
C :: CAPTAIN BLUMBURTT ☐

Answers
Give yourself one point for every correct answer. Make a note of your scores from this round and move on to the next challenge.
17b, 18a, 19b, 20b, 21c, 22c, 23c, 24a

MAGIC SCROLL

INDY CAME ACROSS THIS MAGICAL SCROLL BURIED DEEP WITHIN AN AZTEC PYRAMID. CAN YOU DECIPHER THE CODE TO DISCOVER WHAT THE SCROLL REVEALS? INDY STARTED TO WORK IT OUT BUT THE RUSSIANS FOUND HIS HIDING PLACE AND HE HAD TO MAKE A QUICK GETAWAY!

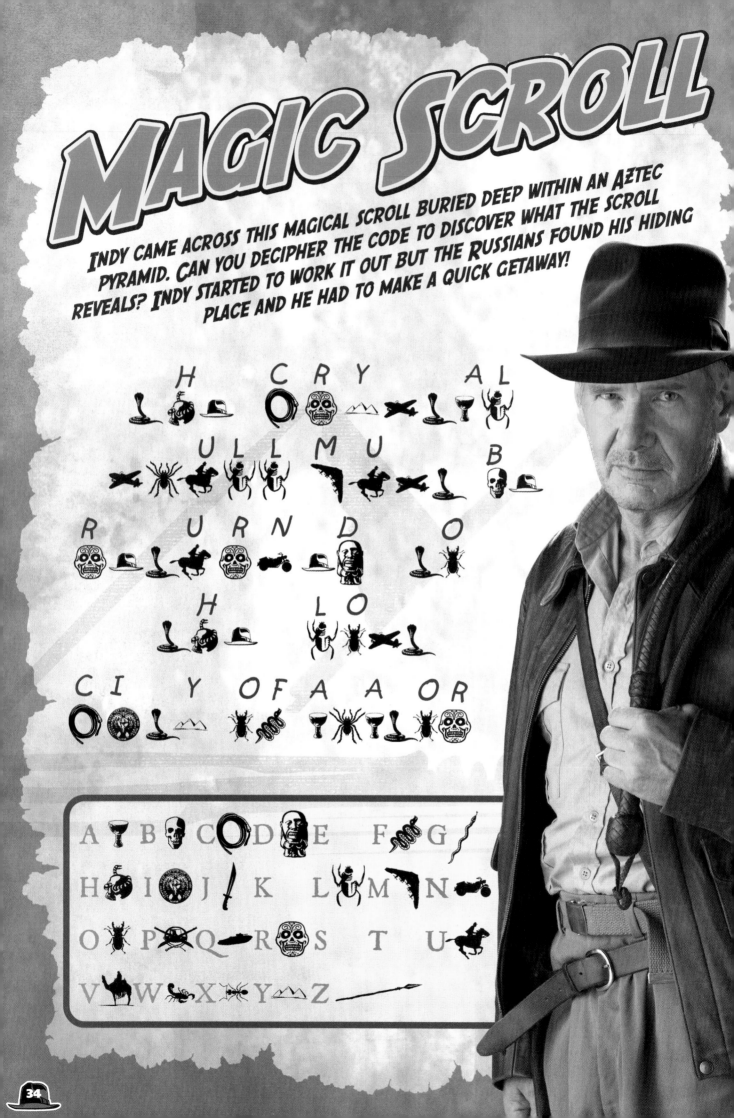

THE TREASURES

The Lost Ark

The Ark of the Covenant is described in the Bible as a sacred container, which held the tablets of stone containing the Ten Commandments.

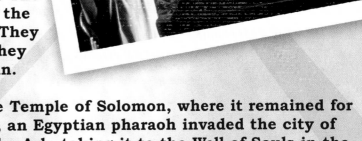

According to the Bible, the Ark was built at the command of God, following a vision had by Moses on Mount Sinai. The Hebrews took the broken pieces of the tablets and put them into the Ark. They carried the Ark with them until they settled in the land of Canaan.

The Ark was placed in the Temple of Solomon, where it remained for many years. However, an Egyptian pharaoh invaded the city of Jerusalem and stole the Ark, taking it to the Well of Souls in the city of Tanis.

Shiva Linga

The Shiva Linga is a symbol for the worship of the Hindu god Shiva. The use of this symbol for worship is an ancient tradition in India.

When Indy arrives in a small Indian village, the Shiva Linga has been stolen by an evil maharajah. The stone has three lines engraved into it, representing the three levels of the universe.

When the stone is stolen, the earth swallows the village crops and the animals lie down and turn to dust. Then, one terrible night, all the village children are kidnapped.

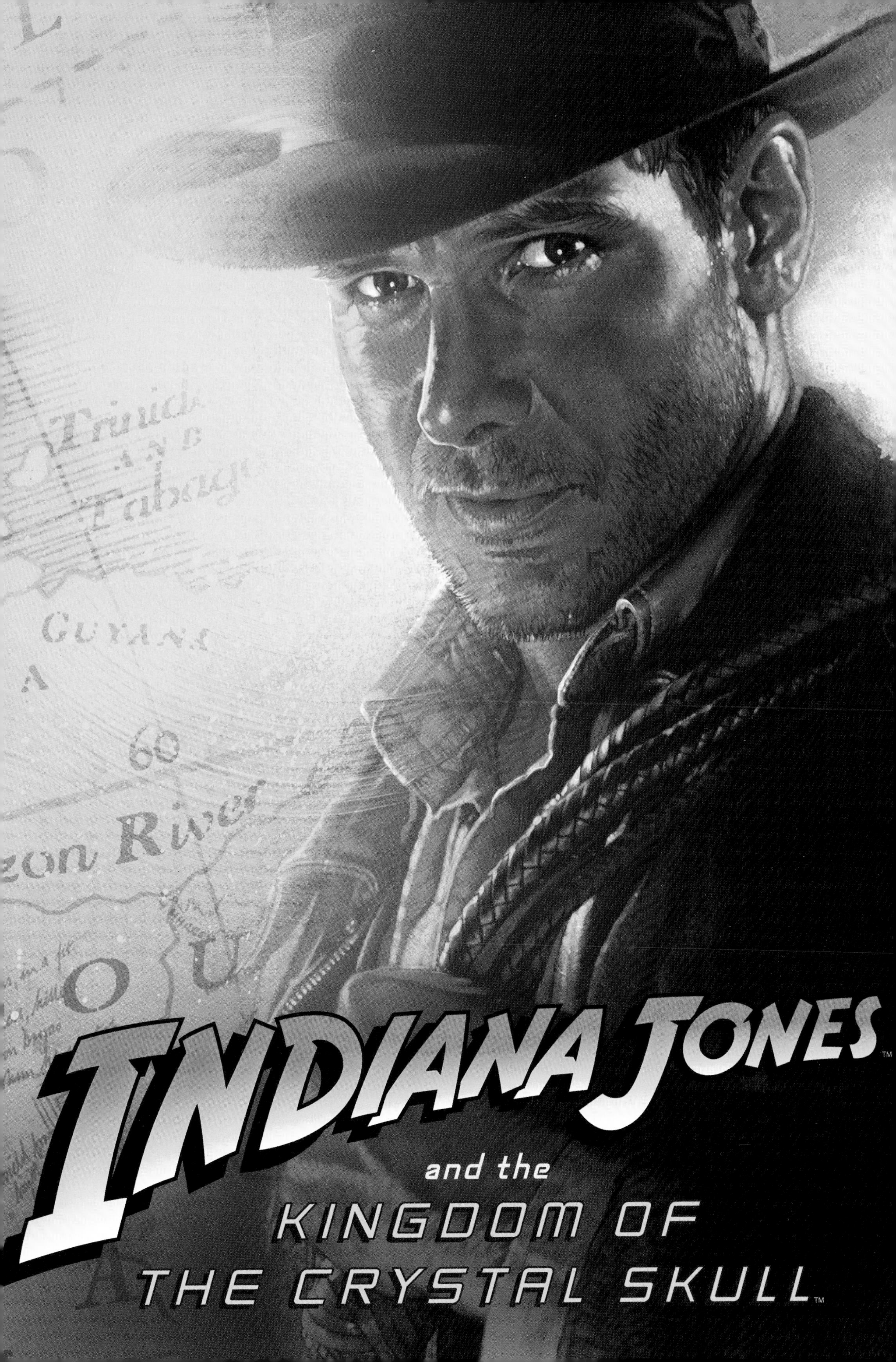
INDIANA JONES™
and the
KINGDOM OF
THE CRYSTAL SKULL™

ADVENTURER QUIZ

Part 4

You have arrived inside the inner sanctum of the Temple of Doom. The Thuggees are right behind you! Answer these questions and escape as quickly as you can!

25

Who says: "You are in a position unsuitable to give orders!"?

A :: WILLIE SCOTT ☐

B :: MOLA RAM ☐

C :: SHORT ROUND ☐

26

Who is this?

A :: WILLIE ☐

B :: MOLA RAM ☐

C :: CHATTAR LAL ☐

27

What is the name of the Thuggee goddess?

A :: CARLY

B :: KALI

C :: SHIVA

28

Who attacks Indy using a voodoo doll?

A :: THE MAHARAJAH

B :: MOLA RAM

C :: WILLIE

29

What is the name of the palace that hides the Temple of Doom?

A :: BUCKINGHAM

B :: REYNOLDS

C :: PANKOT

30

What is Indy forced to drink that sends him into the 'black sleep of Kali'?

A :: KALI'S BLOOD

B :: MOLA RAM'S BLOOD

C :: INDIAN TEA

31

Who says, "I keep telling you, you listen to me more, you live longer!"?

A :: SHORT ROUND

B :: MARCUS BRODY

C :: MOLA RAM

32

Who is this?

A :: SHORT ROUND

B :: LAO CHE

C :: WU HAN

Answers

Give yourself one point for every correct answer. Make a note of your scores from this round and move on to the next challenge.

25b, 26a, 27b, 28a, 29c, 30a, 31b, 32a

39

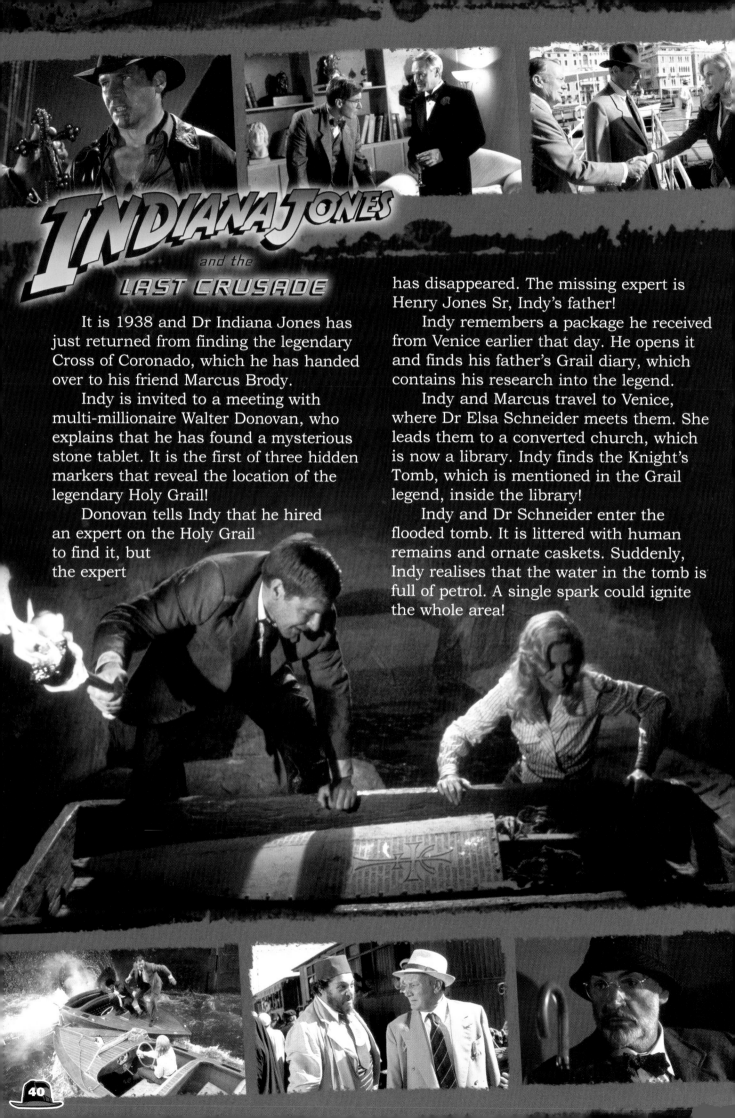

INDIANA JONES

and the
LAST CRUSADE

It is 1938 and Dr Indiana Jones has just returned from finding the legendary Cross of Coronado, which he has handed over to his friend Marcus Brody.

Indy is invited to a meeting with multi-millionaire Walter Donovan, who explains that he has found a mysterious stone tablet. It is the first of three hidden markers that reveal the location of the legendary Holy Grail!

Donovan tells Indy that he hired an expert on the Holy Grail to find it, but the expert has disappeared. The missing expert is Henry Jones Sr, Indy's father!

Indy remembers a package he received from Venice earlier that day. He opens it and finds his father's Grail diary, which contains his research into the legend.

Indy and Marcus travel to Venice, where Dr Elsa Schneider meets them. She leads them to a converted church, which is now a library. Indy finds the Knight's Tomb, which is mentioned in the Grail legend, inside the library!

Indy and Dr Schneider enter the flooded tomb. It is littered with human remains and ornate caskets. Suddenly, Indy realises that the water in the tomb is full of petrol. A single spark could ignite the whole area!

Indy and Dr Schneider find the Knight's Tomb. Indy takes a rubbing of the engraving on the knight's shield. It is the second marker!

Meanwhile, Marcus is attacked by a group of men who throw a lighted match into the tomb, setting the whole place on fire! Indy and the beautiful doctor escape from the tomb, but the men who attacked Marcus are hot on their trail.

After an incredible boat chase through the canals of Venice, Indy discovers that the men are part of an ancient order called the Brotherhood of the Cruciform Sword. For hundreds of years, it has been their job to protect the Grail.

Indy's father is being held prisoner in Brunwald Castle in Austria. Indy instructs Marcus to travel to Turkey and meet his old friend Sallah in the city of Iskenderun. Meanwhile, Indy and Elsa travel to Austria.

Brunwald Castle is occupied by Hitler's Nazi soldiers. It turns out that both Elsa Schneider and Walter Donovan are Nazi spies! The Nazis take the Grail diary and leave Indy and his father to die.

Indy rescues his father and they escape the castle. However, their problems have only just begun!

Indy and his father travel to Berlin and rescue the Grail diary from Dr Schneider. Then they get on a Zeppelin airship that is heading out of Germany. It seems as if the two archaeologists are safe at last.

Suddenly, Indy realises that the ship is turning around and heading back to Germany! Indy and his father jump into the small aircraft at the bottom of the huge balloon, but as they fly away, two Nazi fighter planes appear and open fire.

Indy and his father manage to destroy both the enemy planes. They travel to the Republic of Hatay and meet Indy's old friend, Sallah. Sallah tells them that Marcus has been captured – and he has the map that shows the location of the Grail!

The three men find the Nazis in the desert. The Brotherhood of the Cruciform Sword has also followed the Nazis, but the soldiers massacre them. During the confusion, Indy steals several horses and his father is imprisoned in a Nazi tank with Marcus Brody.

Indy leaps from his horse on to the roof of the tank and pulls his father and Brody out. They are safe, but as Indy fights the soldiers, the tank drops over the edge of a cliff!

Dr Jones Sr, Sallah and Marcus race to the edge of the cliff as Indy hauls himself back up. He had grabbed hold of some overhanging vines as the tank fell! The four men mount their horses and set off to save the Grail.

When the friends arrive in the Canyon of the Crescent Moon, the Nazis are already there – and so is Walter Donovan! The temple entrance is rigged with three booby traps.

Suddenly, the guards spot the adventurers. Donovan orders Indy to go into the temple, but Indy refuses. He will not help the Nazis gain the power of the Grail.

Donovan shoots Indy's father and laughs. He tells Indy that the only way to save his father is to retrieve the Grail. Legend says that the Grail can grant eternal life. Reluctantly, Indy steps into the booby-trapped entrance.

Indy racks his memory. His father discovered clues about how to avoid each of the three traps. Indy just has to remember them all – and work out what they mean before he loses his life!

The first trap is called the 'Breath of God'. The clue is, 'only the penitent man will pass'. Indy drops to his knees as a huge blade flies past his face.

The second trap is called 'Proceed in the Footsteps of the Word'. The floor is covered in lettered tiles. Indy spells out the name of God and crosses the unstable floor.

The third and last trap is called the 'Path Of God'. Indy reaches an opening in the side of a sheer cliff face. There seems to be no way to cross the gap. This requires a leap of faith. Closing his eyes, Indy steps out into the chasm.

Indy feels his foot land on something firm. It was an illusion! There is a footpath across the gap, but it is almost impossible to see because it is made from the same stone as the cliff.

Indy hurries across the bridge and finds a knight kneeling at a table. He has been there for centuries. Donovan and Dr Schneider follow Indy. The walls are lined with chalices. The knight explains that the true Grail will give eternal life, but any of the fake ones will take life away.

Dr Schneider offers to choose for Donovan. She picks an ornate chalice, made of gold and encrusted with jewels. Donovan drinks from it and his face contorts. He screams as his hands wither and wrinkle. As Indy and Dr Schneider watch, Donovan's body decays and turn to dust.

Dr Schneider says that she knew the Grail would not be made from gold. She has turned her back on the Nazis. Indy looks carefully at all the chalices in the room until he sees a wooden one with no decorations. Indy drinks from the chalice, and nothing happens. Indy has chosen the true Grail!

Indy and Dr Schneider run back and Indy makes his

father drink from the chalice. He then pours the holy water on to his father's wound, which heals instantly.

Dr Schneider picks up the chalice and starts to leave the temple. Suddenly the building begins to shake and she drops the chalice. Indy, Dr Jones, Sallah and Marcus escape, but Dr Schneider tries to rescue the Grail. Glory and power is worth more to her than her life, and she dies in the crumbling building.

Indy, Henry, Marcus and Sallah ride off into the sunset. Whatever new adventures are coming their way, as a team they can face anything!

ADVENTURER QUIZ

Part 5

You are doing well, young explorer. You have defeated the Thuggees, but now you must help Indy and his father find the Holy Grail. Do you have what it takes to assist them?

33

In what year does Indy go in search of the Holy Grail?

A :: 1938 ☐
B :: 1939 ☐
C :: 1940 ☐

34

Who is this?

A :: DOCTOR HENRY JONES SR ☐
B :: DOCTOR HENRY JONES JR ☐
C :: WALTER DONOVAN ☐

35

In which Italian city does Indy find the tomb of Sir Richard?

A :: MILAN ☐
B :: NAPLES ☐
C :: VENICE ☐

36

Who says:

"Archaeology is the search for fact... not truth. If it's truth you're looking for, Dr Tyree's philosophy class is right down the hall."?

A :: INDY ☐

B :: DOCTOR HENRY JONES SR ☐

C :: WALTER DONOVAN ☐

37

What is the name of the castle where Indy's father is held prisoner?

A :: DONNINGTON CASTLE ☐

B :: CALSTOCK CASTLE ☐

C :: BRUNWALD CASTLE ☐

38

Kazim is the leader of which order?

A :: BROTHERHOOD OF MAN ☐

B :: BROTHERHOOD OF THE CRUCIFORM SWORD ☐

C :: BROTHERHOOD OF THE ACOLYTES ☐

39

Who is this?

A :: DR ELSA SCHNEIDER ☐

B :: KAZIM ☐

C :: MRS. DONOVAN ☐

40

In which German city does Indy get Adolf Hitler's autograph?

A :: FRANKFURT ☐

B :: BERLIN ☐

C :: COLOGNE ☐

Answers
Give yourself one point for every correct answer. Make a note of your scores from this round and move on to the final challenge.
33a, 34a, 35c, 36a, 37c, 38b, 39a, 40b

ADVENTURER QUIZ Part 6

You have escaped the Nazis for now, but you must travel to Hatay to retrieve the Grail before them! Will you make it on time?

41

What type of transport do Indy and his father use to escape Berlin?

A :: AEROPLANE ☐
B :: BOAT ☐
C :: ZEPPELIN ☐

42

Who says: *"Is there anyone here who speaks English? Or maybe even ancient Greek?"*?

A :: HENRY JONES SR ☐
B :: MARCUS BRODY ☐
C :: SALLAH ☐

43

Who is this?

A :: WALTER DONOVAN ☐
B :: VOGEL ☐
C :: MARCUS BRODY ☐

44

What is the name of the canyon where the temple holding the Grail is located?

A :: CANYON OF THE CRESCENT MOON ☐

B :: CANYON OF THE FULL MOON ☐

C :: CANYON OF THE HALF MOON ☐

45

Who shoots Dr Henry Jones Sr?

A :: DONOVAN ☐

B :: VOGEL ☐

C :: DR ELSA SCHNEIDER ☐

46

Who says: "Don't look at me like that. We both wanted the Grail. I would have done anything to get it. You would have done the same."?

A :: DR ELSA SCHNEIDER ☐

B :: SALLAH ☐

C :: DONOVAN ☐

47

Where does Brody meet up with Sallah?

A :: TANIS ☐

B :: BERLIN ☐

C :: ISKENDERUN ☐

48

Who is this?

A :: FEDORA ☐

B :: VOLGEL ☐

C :: PROFESSOR STANTON ☐

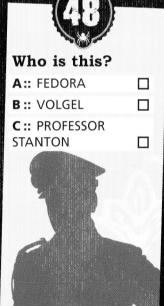

Answers
41c, 42b, 43c, 44a, 45a, 46a, 47c, 48b

Final Score

Now add up all your quiz scores to find out if you are a worthy companion for Indiana Jones!

1-16 - You will need to work a lot harder before you can accompany Indy on his adventures!

17-32 - You are trustworthy and you have courage, but you are not quite as intrepid as Dr Jones!

33-48 - Congratulations! You are intelligent and daring - a worthy companion for Indiana Jones!

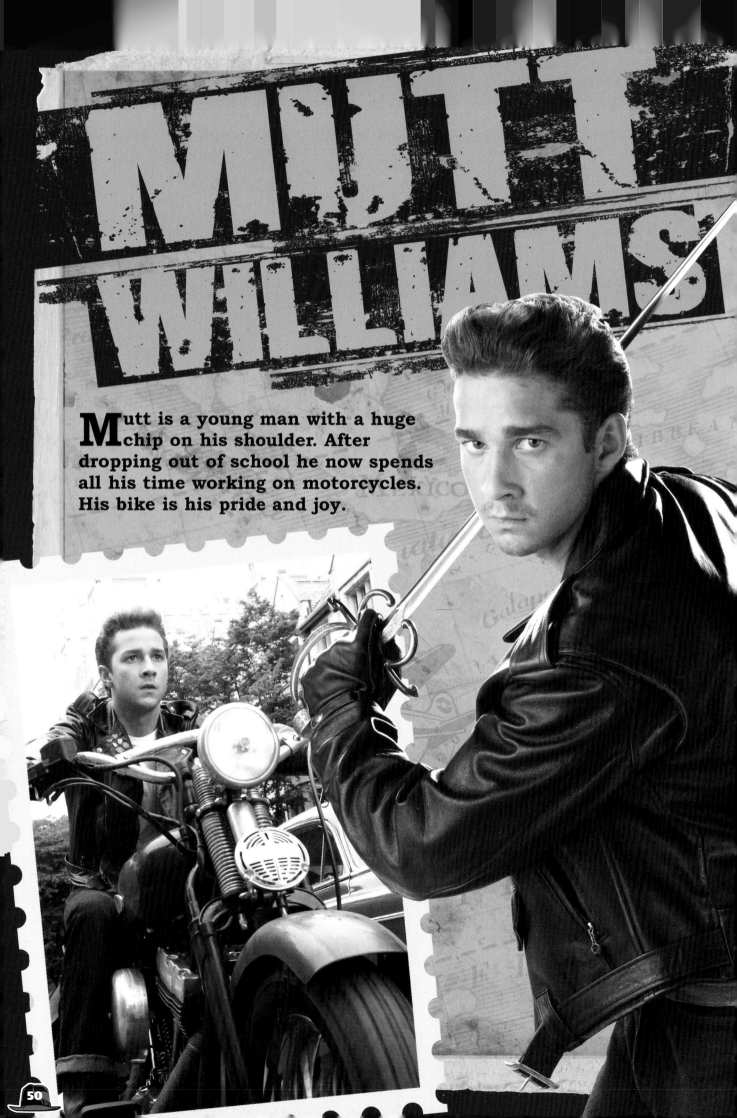

MUTT WILLIAMS

Mutt is a young man with a huge chip on his shoulder. After dropping out of school he now spends all his time working on motorcycles. His bike is his pride and joy.

Mutt's mother is Mary Williams, one of Indy's old girlfriends, although Indy knows her better as Marion Ravenwood. When Marion goes missing in South America, Mutt receives a letter telling him to find Indy and let him know that an old friend, Harold Oxley, has found an important artefact and has been kidnapped.

Mutt finds himself travelling to Peru with Doctor Jones – and getting into all sorts of adventures along the way! He is a skilled fencer and he shares Indy's love of adventure.

MARION RAVENWOOD

Marion is Indy's ex-fiancé and the daughter of the world-renowned archaeologist, Dr. Abner Ravenwood.

Abner was a mentor to Indy, and the two often accompanied each other on archaeological digs. When Marion met Indy they fell in love, but their relationship was fiery and Abner did not approve of it.

Marion is a strong woman who has never been intimidated by any man. She is completely self-reliant, but even after not seeing or speaking to Indy for over twenty years, there is still a spark between them when they meet again.

HAROLD OXLEY

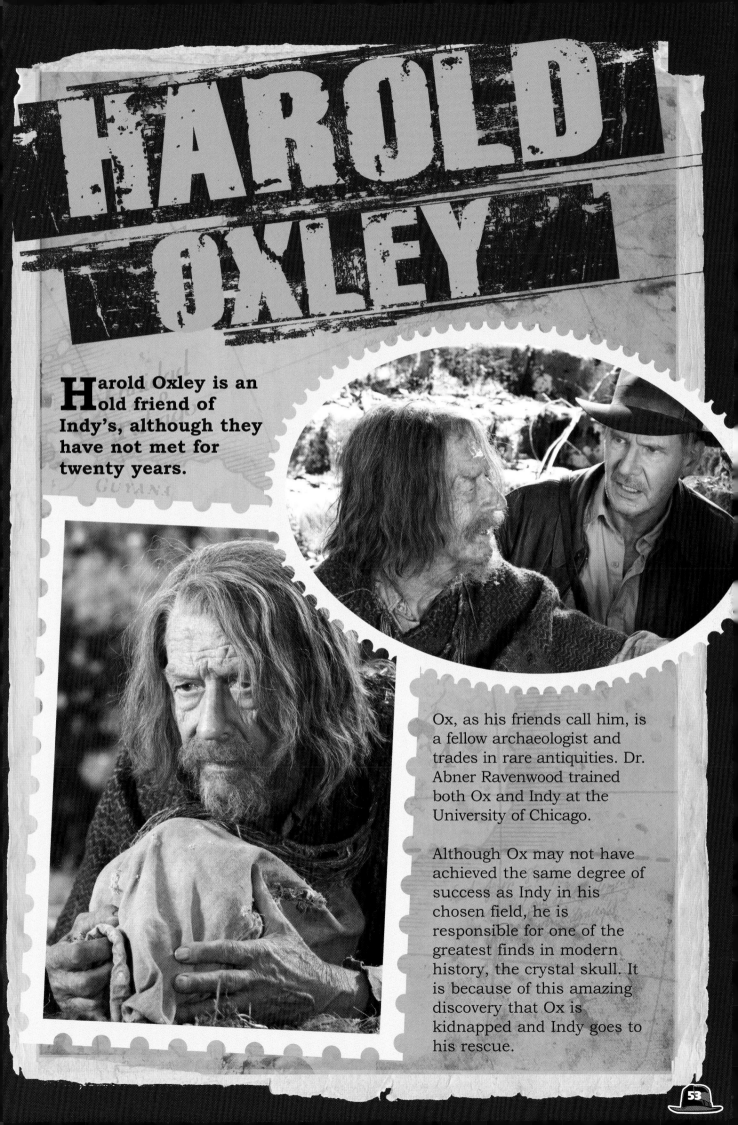

Harold Oxley is an old friend of Indy's, although they have not met for twenty years.

Ox, as his friends call him, is a fellow archaeologist and trades in rare antiquities. Dr. Abner Ravenwood trained both Ox and Indy at the University of Chicago.

Although Ox may not have achieved the same degree of success as Indy in his chosen field, he is responsible for one of the greatest finds in modern history, the crystal skull. It is because of this amazing discovery that Ox is kidnapped and Indy goes to his rescue.

DR IRINA SPALKO

Irina is a Russian agent from the Eastern Ukraine.

She has had a very successful career in the KGB, partly thanks to her psychic ability to see events before they happen. She has been awarded the Order of Lenin on three separate occasions and has also received a medal honouring her as a Hero of Socialist Labour.

Her psychic abilities are not very strong and can be unreliable. Irina is skilled in the art of swordsmanship and carries her faithful fencing sword with her at all times. She is as beautiful as she is deadly.

ANTONIN DOVCHENKO

Antonin Dovchenko is a Russian soldier and Dr Spalko's right-hand man.

He is a grizzled war veteran who has been involved in many of the KGB's most vital missions.

Dovchenko is an intimidating man and he enjoys inflicting pain on others. He controls his unit through fear and violence and is undyingly loyal to his country.

GEORGE MC HALE

Mac is an old friend and colleague of Indy's.

They worked together for the military intelligence agencies of their respective countries. They have known each other for over fifteen years and have been together in some tough spots.

Mac has a healthy interest in archaeology but he is driven more by the possibility of making money. Mac's greed sometimes leads him to make wrong decisions and this sometimes makes Indy a little wary of his old friend.

THE CRYSTAL SKULL

The crystal skull is a carving made by an ancient civilisation called the Ugha.

At the instruction of their gods 7,000 years ago, the Ugha built a city of pure gold, deep within the Amazon rainforest. They named the city Akator, and invented technology that was thousands of years ahead of its time.

In 1546, a conquistador called Francesco de Orellana disappeared in the Amazon while looking for Akator. He was known as the Gilded Man because of his love of gold. In the 1920s, a British explorer named Percy Fawcett also disappeared.

Over the years, several crystal skulls appeared around the world and have been exhibited by several museums. However, when Ox discovers a skull in Peru, he believes it to be different from all the others. This one has psychic powers!

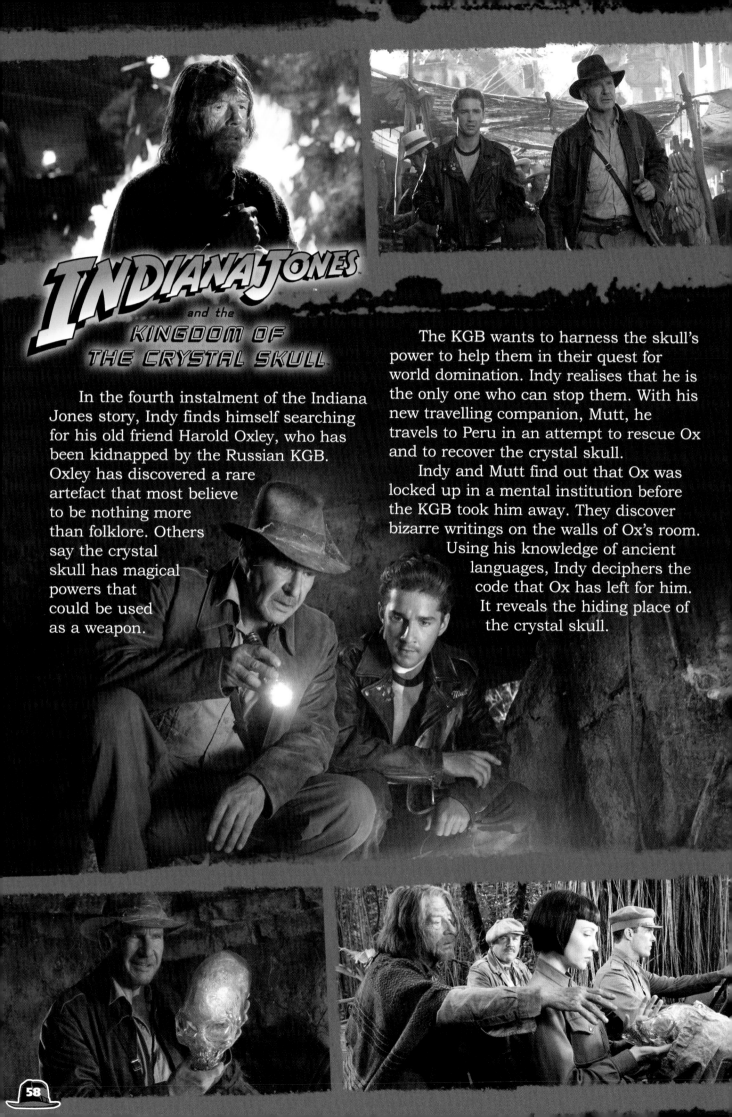

INDIANA JONES

and the
KINGDOM OF THE CRYSTAL SKULL

In the fourth instalment of the Indiana Jones story, Indy finds himself searching for his old friend Harold Oxley, who has been kidnapped by the Russian KGB. Oxley has discovered a rare artefact that most believe to be nothing more than folklore. Others say the crystal skull has magical powers that could be used as a weapon.

The KGB wants to harness the skull's power to help them in their quest for world domination. Indy realises that he is the only one who can stop them. With his new travelling companion, Mutt, he travels to Peru in an attempt to rescue Ox and to recover the crystal skull.

Indy and Mutt find out that Ox was locked up in a mental institution before the KGB took him away. They discover bizarre writings on the walls of Ox's room.

Using his knowledge of ancient languages, Indy deciphers the code that Ox has left for him. It reveals the hiding place of the crystal skull.

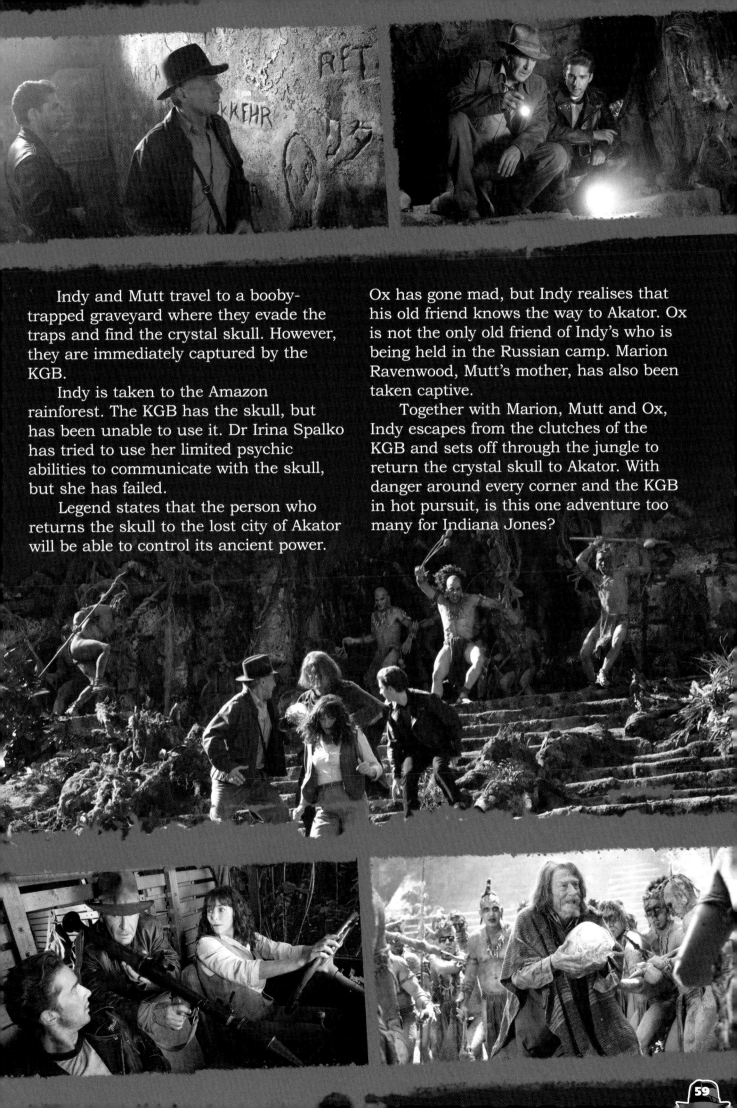

Indy and Mutt travel to a booby-trapped graveyard where they evade the traps and find the crystal skull. However, they are immediately captured by the KGB.

Indy is taken to the Amazon rainforest. The KGB has the skull, but has been unable to use it. Dr Irina Spalko has tried to use her limited psychic abilities to communicate with the skull, but she has failed.

Legend states that the person who returns the skull to the lost city of Akator will be able to control its ancient power.

Ox has gone mad, but Indy realises that his old friend knows the way to Akator. Ox is not the only old friend of Indy's who is being held in the Russian camp. Marion Ravenwood, Mutt's mother, has also been taken captive.

Together with Marion, Mutt and Ox, Indy escapes from the clutches of the KGB and sets off through the jungle to return the crystal skull to Akator. With danger around every corner and the KGB in hot pursuit, is this one adventure too many for Indiana Jones?

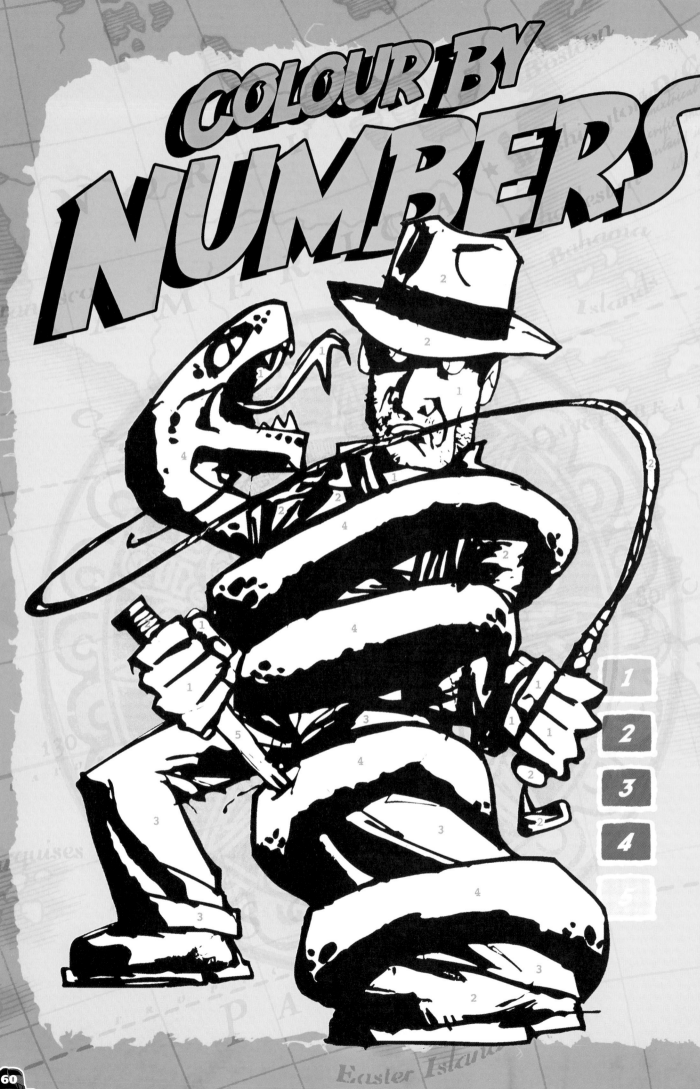

WHICH WHIP?

ONLY INDY'S WHIP LEADS TO THE CRYSTAL SKULL. CAN YOU WORK OUT WHICH ONE IT IS? BE CAREFUL - IF YOU CHOOSE THE WRONG WHIP YOU WILL FIND BOOBY TRAPS INSTEAD!

ODD ICONS

CHECK OUT THESE FOUR ICONS. THEY MAY ALL LOOK THE SAME, BUT IN EACH ROW ONE IS SLIGHTLY DIFFERENT FROM THE OTHERS. CAN YOU SPOT WHICH ONE IT IS?

1.
2.
3.
4.
5.
6.

THE EYES HAVE IT!

CAN YOU NAME ALL THESE BAD GUYS JUST BY LOOKING AT THEIR EYES? TRY TO GET ALL THE ANSWERS RIGHT QUICKLY, OR YOU AND INDY COULD BE IN TROUBLE!

DR ELSA SCHNEIDER   DIETRICH   MOLA RAM   SPALKO   DOVCHENKO
WALTER DONOVAN   BELLOQ   CHATTAR LAL   TOHT   LAO CHE

ANSWERS

Page 14 - Word Search

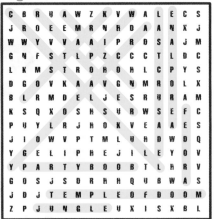

Page 15 - Cross Word

The Cross Word grid contains:
Down 1: THE WELL OF SOULS
Down 2: BELLOQ
Down 3: MARION
Down 5: KATANGA
Down 7: DIETRICH
Across 4: SALLAH
Across 6: TOHT
Across 8: SNAKES

Pages 18-19 - Spot the Difference

Pages 22-23 - Mystical Maze

Page 30 - Code Cracker

WE HAVE TRACKED DOCTOR JONES TO CAIRO, EGYPT. WE BELIEVE HE WILL BE MEETING HIS OLD FRIEND SALLAH IN AN ATTEMPT TO DISCOVER THE LOCATION OF ARK. WE WILL INTERCEPT HIM AS HE BOARDS A PADDLE STEAMER ON THE RIVER NILE. WE CAN NOT LET HIM REACH HIS DESTINATION. THIS IS A DIRECT ORDER FROM DIETRICH.

Page 31 - Skull Squares

YOU SHOULD HAVE COLLECTED 2 TREASURES

Page 34 - Magic Scroll

THE CRYSTAL SKULL MUST BE RETURNED TO THE LOST CITY OF AKATOR

Page 64 - Which Whip?

NUMBER 3

Page 65 - Odd Icons

Page 66-67 - The Eyes Have It!

1. DOVCHENKO
2. TOHT
3. DR ELSA SCHNEIDER
4. SPALKO
5. CHATTAR LAL
6. LAO CHE
7. DIETRICH
8. WALTER DONOVAN
9. MOLA RAM
10. BELLOQ